This book

belongs to...

The
Orchard Fairies

Illustrated by

Margaret W. Tarrant

Original poetry by

Marion St. John Webb

Series Editor

Fiona Waters

·MARGARET TARRANT'S·
FAIRIES & FLOWERS

First published in this format in 2003 by
The Medici Society Ltd
Grafton House, Hyde Estate Road, London NW9 6JZ

Copyright © The Medici Society Ltd 2003 / 1928

First published in 1928 by The Medici Society Ltd
1 3 5 7 9 10 8 6 4 2

A catalogue record for this book is available from the British Library.

ISBN 0 85503 261 8

Margaret Tarrant's original artworks have been rescanned for this re-designed edition.

Designed by Tony Potter Publishing Ltd

Printed in Singapore

The
Orchard Fairies

Contents

A Fairy in Disguise ...   7

When the Wind Blows ...   13

Fancy Dress ...   19

The Greedy Goblin ...   25

In the Cupboard ...   31

What the Moon didn't see ...   35

Margaret Winifred Tarrant ...   42

A Fairy in Disguise

Fairy in the pear tree,
All among the flowers,
Why do you sit watching
The butterflies for hours?
As they flutter round you
I can see you smile,
And you whisper secrets,
Laughing all the while.
Fairy in the pear tree,
Please sing a little song.
Tell me all about it,
It won't take very long.

The Pear Blossom Fairy sings:
I sit on a branch in the pear
  blossom tree,
While butterflies flitter and flutter
  around me.
They really are fairies, but they're
  all in disguise,
For they've turned themselves into
  butterflies!
I've asked them the secret, oh, what
  must I do
To turn myself into a butterfly, too?

And now they have told me!
So if you should see
A butterfly here that looks
rather like me,
You'll know what has
happened, and won't be
surprised.
For a butterfly's always a fairy
disguised.

Fairy in the pear tree,
Children sometimes say
That they can't find fairies
In our world today.
Some of them see fairies
Everywhere they go.
But all those who *can't* see
Really ought to know,
Fairy in the pear tree,
What you've told to me:
Butterflies are the fairies
That *everyone* can see!

When the Wind Blows

The wind came whispering
   through the wood,
And down the lane where the
   orchard stood.
It glided softly among the trees,
Such a polite, well-behaved little
   breeze.
"Excuse me," it said if it made a
   bough sway
As quietly it passed by, on its way.

But the goblins who hid in the
   hedge at night,
They frowned and said, "It's silly
   to be so polite!"

They gazed at the apples that grew
  on the trees,
And muttered, "Oh, what is the use
  of a breeze!"

The wind came blustering through
   the wood,
And down the lane where the
   orchard stood.
It shook the trees till it made
   them quail,
Roaring and howling, such a
   terrible gale.
It snatched at the apples and flung
   them around,
Until they lay scattered all over
   the ground.

And the goblins who hid in the
  hedge ran out,
And picked up the apples that lay
  all about.
They carried them home in great
  delight,
Shouting, "This rude wind for us
  was just right!"

Fancy Dress

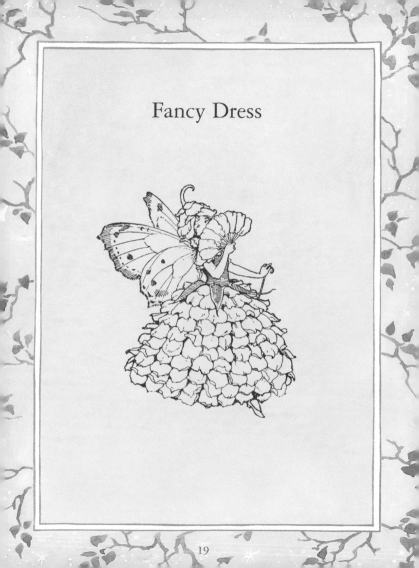

"You're a very naughty fairy,"
Cried the angry little gnome.
"I live here in the apple tree,
Don't come and spoil my home!
Why do you shake the tree?
You'll make the blossom fall.
You really don't deserve to be
A fairy girl at all!"

"Well, I'm sorry to annoy you,"
Said the fairy, "but I've planned
To make myself a dress of flowers;
I hope you'll understand.
A dress of apple blossom frills
To dance in at the ball.
So let me shake the bough again,
Just one more time, that's all."

"No, you shan't, you naughty fairy!"
Cried the gnome, so angry now
That in a rage he stamped his foot
Upon the flowery bough.
This shook a dozen blossoms off.
"Ah! Twelve more frills of stuff!
I thank you, sir," the fairy laughed,
"*Now* I have enough!"

The Greedy Goblin

Three fine plums on a fine plum tree.
A goblin there did find them.
"I'll keep these plums for myself," said he,
"I won't let people find them."
He made a little leafy screen
And kept the plums from being seen.

Three fine plums on a fine plum tree
Grew bigger and riper and stronger.
"They must grow bigger still for me.
I'll wait a little longer!"
The goblin watched and chased off fast
All other fairies who came past.

Three ripe plums on a fine plum tree
Grew riper every morning.
Then one plum fell, then two, then three,
Without the slightest warning!
All spoilt and squashed the ripe plums lay
Upon the orchard ground that day.

The goblin sat in the fine plum tree
And grumbled about the matter.
"He was a greedy thing, you see,"
He heard the fairies chatter.
"I'm sure he will be feeling sad,
But it all comes of being so bad."

The goblin frowned and shook his head.
"Oh, go away," he crossly said.
"I can see now that I was wrong
To hide those plums away so long.
A plum's no use when past its prime.
I'll eat them quickly another time!"

In the Cupboard

Cherries in a basket,
   Store them all away
In a fairy cupboard
For a rainy day.
Cherries in a cupboard
And the fairies say,
"Once we saw them growing,
In the month of May."

Fairies in a basket,
Store them in a row
In the nursery cupboard,
Before you older grow.
Fairies in a cupboard,
But you'll always know
Once you saw them flying,
Not so long ago.

THE
FAIRIES ORCHARD
TRESPASSERS
WILL BE
PROSECUTED

M. W. Tarrant

What the Moon didn't see

The Man in the Moon peeped
over the hill
And looked at the orchard, where all
was still.
He glanced at the river, gazed down
the lane,
And then looked round at the
orchard again.
His eyebrows shot up, and his eyes
gave a blink.
"Oh, ho!" said the Man in the Moon,
"I should think
There's going to be trouble down
there tonight."

And that's where the Man in the
  Moon was right.
For down by the gate, where the
  shadows lay deep,
Were hundreds of goblins all waiting
  to creep
Into the orchard to have a good meal
Of apples and anything else they
  could steal.
The Man in the Moon looked round
  and about,
And then all of a sudden, he heard a
  great shout!

The fairies who guarded the orchard
  by night
Had seen all the goblins, and sprung
  up to fight.
The goblins rushed out, bright-eyed
  for the fray,
And the battle began without more
  delay.

Such shouting there was, such a
  hullabaloo,
Such pushing and shoving, and such
  a to-do,
That no-one knew who was who; and
  so each
Pushed everyone else he could
  possibly reach.

The Man in the Moon looked down
  with a grin,
And wondered if this side or that side
  would win.
The goblins, though greedy, were all
  very brave,
While the fairies were frantic the
  orchard to save.

And so they fought on, till so tired
they all grew
That what they were fighting for
nobody knew.
And nobody knew who was wrong
and who right,
One after another, they dropped out
of the fight.
"And so," thought the Man in the
Moon, "it all ends.
The battle's forgotten, and now
they'll make friends!"

But that's where the Man in the
Moon was wrong.
The fight had been fierce, and the
fight had been long,

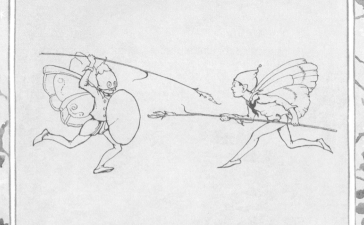

And while they were fighting with
   foot and with fist,
The fairies had made so much noise
   that they'd missed
What had happened behind in the
   orchard, you see.
The wood elves had crawled in and
   robbed every tree!

Margaret Winifred Tarrant (1888 - 1959)

'Every time a child says, " I don't believe in fairies," ' warned Peter Pan, 'there is a little fairy somewhere that falls down dead.' By her paintings Margaret Tarrant did as much to encourage children's belief in fairies as J M Barrie did by his writings. Born in London in 1888, the only child of artist Percy Tarrant and his wife Sarah, Margaret excelled at art from an early age, and she was only 19 when she received her first, very prestigious, commission, from J M Dent & Sons: to illustrate Charles Kingsley's much-loved children's classic, *The Water Babies*, which was first published in 1863.

Her delicate, charming pictures matched the spirit of the story perfectly and earned her a string of new commissions: *Nursery Rhymes* (1914 and 1923), *Alice in Wonderland* (1916) and *Hans Andersen's Fairy Tales* (1917) for Ward Lock & Co., plus postcards for Oxford University Press.

Margaret Tarrant illustrated some 20 books for George G. Harrap & Co. between 1915 and 1929, but an even more important publishing relationship began in 1920, when she completed her first pieces for The Medici Society. This was to prove a long and fruitful connection, resulting in most of her best-known work. In the 1920s, for example, she illustrated this highly successful series of fairy books for the company, written by the poet and author Marion St John Webb. Her picture of Peter's Friends, inspired by J M Barrie's *Peter Pan* stories and the statue in Kensington Gardens, proved so popular when it appeared in 1921 that it had to be reproduced many times.

The dusk of the nineteenth and dawn of the twentieth centuries were magical times for fairy lovers. Fascination with fairy lore was widespread, reaching unprecedented heights in 1922 when Sir Arthur Conan Doyle

Peter's Friends

published *The Coming of the Fairies*, containing 'photographs' of fairies taken by two young girls in a Yorkshire village, which were later proved to be hoaxes. The story was actually a fascinating deception, which was believed by many reputable people. The mystery was not solved until towards the end of the twentieth century, when the girls involved, now elderly ladies, explained what had really happened.

In 1922, Margaret Tarrant's *Do You Believe in Fairies?* showed two children encircled by a ring of fairies, which caught the public excitement already created by Sir Arthur Conan Doyle's book. This interest was mirrored in an outpouring of art

and literature. Children's books cultivated belief in fairies: they were used in religious teaching, magazines were devoted to them, and captivating new works appeared, most notably J M Barrie's *Peter Pan* and *Peter Pan in*

Do You Believe in Fairies?

Kensington Gardens. Rudyard Kipling wrote *Rewards and Fairies* and even Beatrix Potter embraced the subject in *The Fairy Caravan*.

Margaret Tarrant was one of those most associated with the depiction of fairies in the 1920s and 1930s, together with her friend and sketching partner, Cicely Mary Barker (1895 - 1973). Both began to use Art Nouveau and Arts and Crafts elements in their work, and in Tarrant's paintings a breathtaking attention to detail - diaphanous wings with the intricate tracery of a dragonfly's wings - is a testament to the reality of fairies, imaginary or otherwise.

During her life Margaret Tarrant tackled a wide range of subjects and won special acclaim for those, such as *All Things Wise and Wonderful*, with a religious theme. But her forte was fairies, for in her evocation of these ethereal figures she could express her love for children, wild flowers and dance, of all that was beautiful and pure.

Margaret Tarrant's fairies have a unique fluidity and balletic grace that expressed her delight in the free-flowing dance invented by Isadora Duncan. She was very much a free spirit herself, flying along the country lanes around her home in Surrey on an ancient bicycle, leaping off impulsively to sketch meticulously from life to capture the likeness of a child or plant. She never married, but she attracted many friends by her generosity, energy and zest for life. Perhaps it was this childlike enthusiasm and innocence, combined with a special kind of imagination, that gave her a natural affinity with fairies.

The Lily Pool

Much missed when she died in 1959, Margaret Tarrant left a lasting legacy in charming pictures that seem as fresh today as the day they were painted, and still enchant new generations with their glimpses into a secret fairy world.